STECK-VAUGHN

PAIR-IT BOOKS™

GARDEN COLORS

Written by Gare Thompson
Illustrated by Thomas Boll

STECK-VAUGHN
COMPANY

A Division of Harcourt Brace & Company

Red flowers

Blue flowers

3

Pink flowers

Yellow flowers

5

Orange flowers

Purple flowers

Surprise!